Date ..../........../..........

How Many?

Today, Martin has 50 pages of his book left to read. He started the book 2 days ago and read one third of it, and yesterday he read another 30 pages.

How many pages are there in Martin's book?

AF729302

Teacher notes

Date ..../........../..........

Comparing Earnings

This table shows how much some top tennis players have earned in their careers.

Tennis Player	Career Earnings
Andy Harrison	£14 532 353
Ben Murphy	£11 435 294
Caitlin Lebowski	£14 055 882
Dwayn Latoye	£13 653 234
Ehani Tahir	£14 067 853
Frankie Santiago	£13 102 941

Can you put them in descending order to show who has earned the most and who has earned the least?

Tennis Player	Career Earnings

Write in words the amount earned by the richest player.

Teacher notes

numicon

Number, Pattern and Calculating

Explorer 6a Progress Book

Name .... Class ....

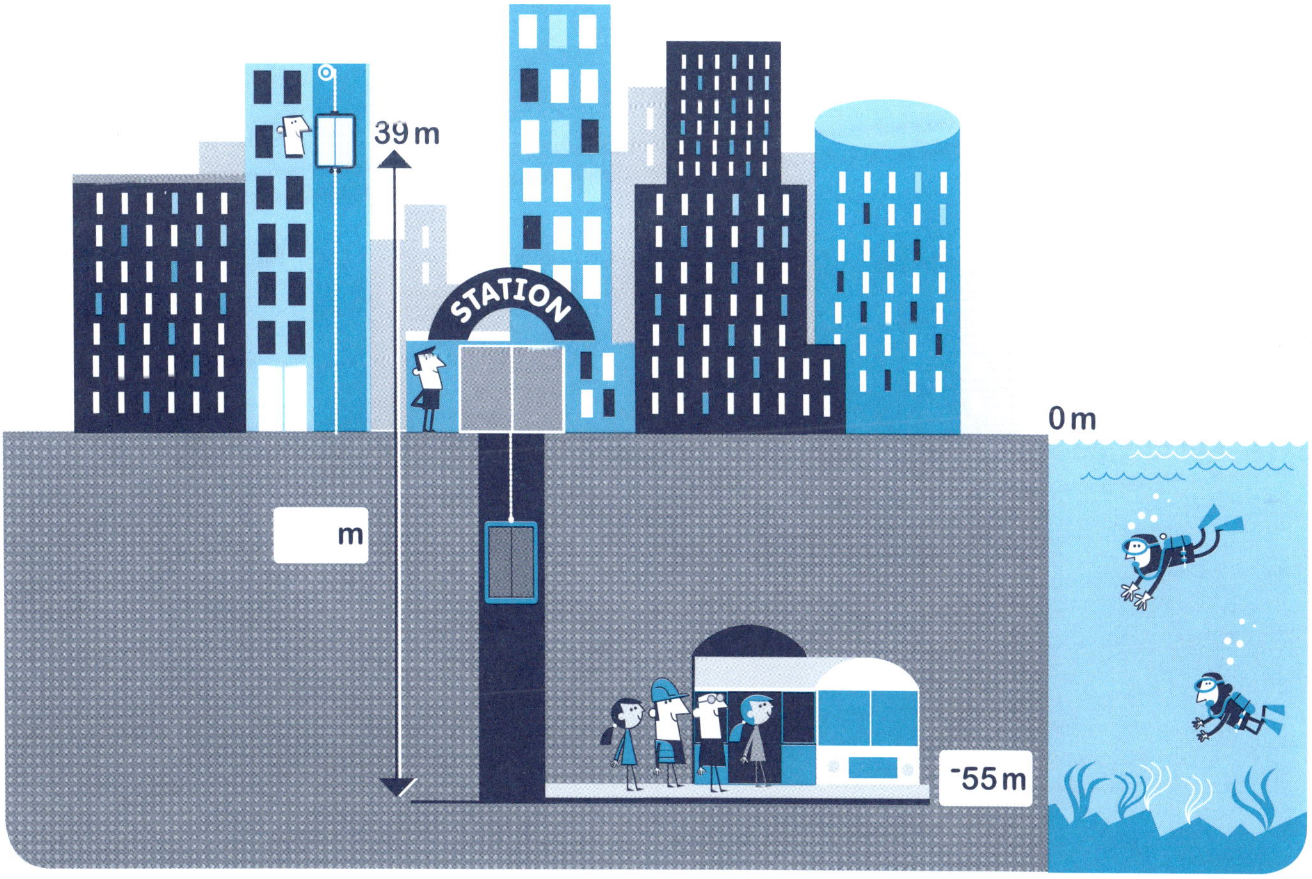

OXFORD

Date ..../........../..........

How Much?

Olive, Sreya and Vicki were having lunch. Olive and Sreya each had a carton of orange juice, but Vicki forgot hers. Olive gave Vicki a quarter of her juice and Sreya gave Vicki half of hers. Vicki ended up with 225 ml in her cup.

If Olive and Sreya both had the same-sized cartons to begin with, how much juice did each carton contain?

Teacher notes

Have ready: base-ten apparatus, two Numicon Spinners with 0–4 and 5–9 overlays or a 0–9 dice

Date ..../........../..........

Getting the Closest

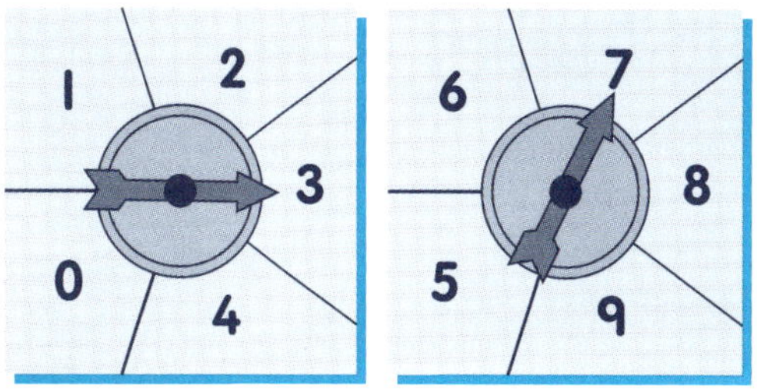

You want to make a number as close as possible to this target number:

4 194 304

Spin either or both of the spinners until you have 7 numbers. Each time you spin, decide where to place the digit to get as close as possible to the target number.

How could you rearrange your numbers to get even closer to the target number?

Teacher notes

Date ..../........../..........

Sea Level

This table shows the heights above and below sea level of some geographical features that are underwater and on land.

Shipwreck	$^{-}102$ m
Mountain	610 m
Skyscraper	265 m
Coral reef	$^{-}46$ m

Can you work out the height difference between each pair of geographical features?

Teacher notes

Date ..../........../..........

Guess the Numbers

The difference between two 5-digit numbers is 1500 and the total is a multiple of 5. What two numbers could they be?

What other two numbers could they be?

Teacher notes

Date ..../........../..........

Using Factors to Multiply

Leah is trying to work out the calculation 24 × 25.

Using factors, how many different ways can you solve this calculation mentally? You can use brackets to show which multiplying calculation you will do first.

Leah has thought of one way:

$6 \times (4 \times 25) =$

Teacher notes

Date ..../........../..........

Doughnut Divide

Sam needs to package his doughnuts in boxes of 12. There are 180 doughnuts in total. Can you work out how many boxes he will need?

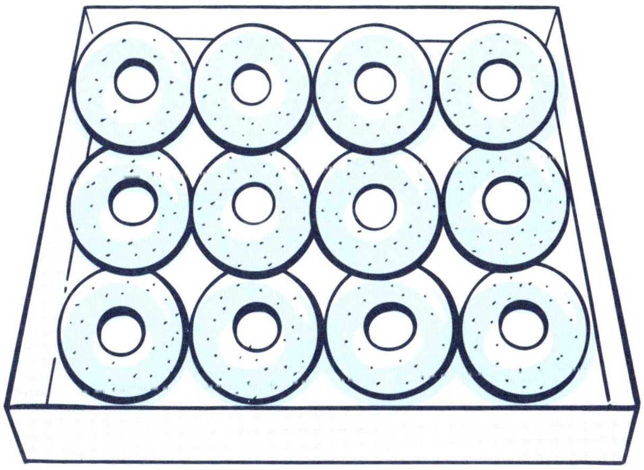

He also makes cupcakes and sells them in boxes of 9. There are 171 cupcakes. Can you find out how many boxes he will need?

Teacher notes

Date ..../........../..........

Using Factors

Kate said she worked out this multiplying sentence in her head, using factors.

Can you explain how she might have done this?

$$75 \times 24$$

Teacher notes

Date ..../........../..........

Flower Arranging

Anjali is making flower arrangements to decorate the entrance hall for a special occasion. She has 32 roses, 24 freesias and 16 carnations. She wants each arrangement to be identical. So, for example, there must be the same number of carnations used in every arrangement.

What is the largest number of arrangements she can make if she uses every flower?

Teacher notes

Date ..../........../..........

Rainfall

4 children monitored rainfall across different areas of their town. They each used the same-sized rain gauge in their gardens. This table shows how full the gauges were after one week.

Which garden had the most rainfall?

Garden	Gauge level
Rosie's garden	$\frac{3}{5}$ full
Tom's garden	$\frac{5}{6}$ full
Joanna's garden	$\frac{2}{3}$ full
Sunil's garden	$\frac{7}{10}$ full

Can you order the amounts and show the fractions with a common denominator?

Garden	Gauge level

Teacher notes

Have ready: Numicon 1–30 Numeral Cards

Date ..../........../..........

Simplifying Fractions

First shuffle your Numeral Cards. Make a fraction like this by turning over a card to give you the numerator, then turn over another to give the denominator.

$$\frac{8}{24}$$

Can it be simplified to an equivalent fraction?

Keep a record of your fractions here. Keep going until you have used all the cards.

Teacher notes

Date ..../........../..........

How Long?

Have you been alive for a million hours?

How many hours have you been alive, to the nearest 100?

Teacher notes

Date ..../........../..........

Estimating Answers

$$28 \cdot 5 \times 4 \cdot 5 = ?$$

Can you round this calculation in different ways to find 2 whole numbers, as close as possible, which the exact answer must lie between?

Which of your estimates is furthest away from the exact answer?

Teacher notes

Date ..../........../..........

Football Fans

Two football teams are playing in a match at a stadium. There are 47 762 Rovers supporters and 38 628 City supporters.

How many supporters are there altogether?

How many more Rovers supporters are there than City supporters?

Teacher notes

Have ready: base-ten apparatus

Date ..../........../..........

Missing Digits

There are two numbers involved in an adding or subtracting calculation. One of the numbers has 5 in the hundredths column and one has 6 in the tenths column.

The answer to the calculation is 1·67. What could the calculation be? Use the calculation layout to help you.

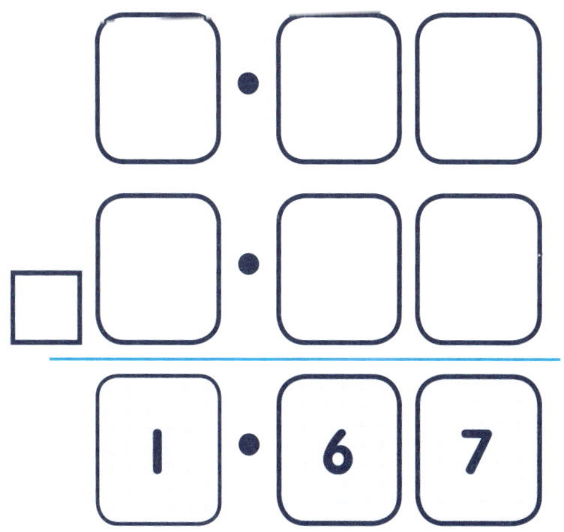

Can you find another way of making the calculation correct?

Teacher notes

Date ..../........../..........

Sale Prices

Eryn's mum bought her a pair of boots in a 20% off sale. She paid £36. What was the full price of the boots originally?

Teacher notes

Date ..../........./.........

School Hours

Janek's school day is from 9 a.m. until 3 p.m. What percentage of his whole day (24 hours) does he spend at school?

Teacher notes

Have ready: ruler, extra paper

Date ..../........../..........

Animal Area

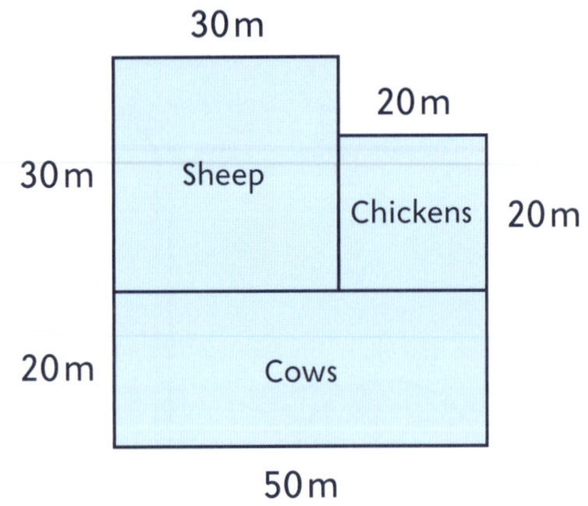

A farmer has put together some pens for her animals. She wants to work out how much space they will take up altogether.

Can you write a calculation to work out the total area of the enclosures?

The farmer needs 3 new enclosures. Can you draw the 3 enclosures for this calculation, ensuring that all enclosures are attached to at least one other? What is the total area of her enclosures?

$$40\,m^2 + 30\,m \times 40\,m + 30\,m \times 60\,m$$

Can you find another way to join these enclosures?

Teacher notes

Date ..../........../..........

Number Totals

How many different totals can you make, using the digits and symbols below? You can use the symbols more than once but you can only use each digit once in any calculation. Use brackets where appropriate.

6 5 8 × ÷ + − =

What is the biggest number you can make?

What is the smallest number you can make?

Teacher notes

My Learning Log

Date ..../........../..........

I know how to...

Date ..../........../..........

I know these facts:

Date ..../........./.........

I can use maths in everyday life when...

Date ..../........./.........

Reflections.

My favourite maths was...

I would like more time to think about...

I felt proud when...

numicon

Number, Pattern and Calculating

Explorer 6a

Progress Book

Can you write in the box how far the man travels down to the station?

Your **Explorer Progress Book 6a** contains:

- Fun activities that give you a chance to show what you understand and what you are thinking.
- Learning Logs where you can record what you know and what you can do.

Say what your favourite piece of work was.

Say what you need more time to think about.

Say what you were most proud of.

Information for your teacher

The activities in this book match the activity groups in the Teaching Resource Handbook for Number, Pattern and Calculating 6. In the top right-hand corner of each page, you can see which activity group it matches.

A range of apparatus should be freely available to children as they work on the activities. The 'Have ready' box at the top of the page shows specific resource requirements where appropriate.

Use the 'Teacher notes' section on each page to give children feedback.

OXFORD
UNIVERSITY PRESS

Great Clarendon Street, Oxford, OX2 6DP, United Kingdom

Oxford University Press is a department of the University of Oxford. It furthers the University's objective of excellence in research, scholarship, and education by publishing worldwide. Oxford is a registered trade mark of Oxford University Press in the UK and in certain other countries

Typeset by Phoenix Photosetting, Chatham
Figurative artworks by Adrian Barclay
Technical artworks by Phoenix Photosetting, Chatham
Cover artwork by David Semple
Written by Jayne Campling, Adella Osborne and Dr Tony Wing

This edition published 2016

ISBN 978-0-19-830506-4

4 6 8 10 9 7 5 3

Printed in China by Golden Cup

OXFORD
UNIVERSITY PRESS

How to get in touch:
web www.oxfordprimary.co.uk
email primary.enquiries@oup.com
tel. +44 (0) 1536 452610
fax +44 (0) 1865 313472

ISBN 978-0-19-830506-4

9 780198 305064